What's Wrong with a Pet Dinosaur?

ISBN 978-1-7375556-0-5 (hardcover)
ISBN 978-1-7375556-1-2 (paperback)
ISBN 978-1-7375556-2-9 (epub)
ISBN 978-1-7375556-3-6 (kindle)

Publisher's Cataloging In Publication Data:
Names: Philips, Tony, 1969- author, illustrator.
Title: What's wrong with a pet dinosaur? : poems and drawings /
by Tony Philips.
Description: Chicago, IL : Idle Brains Publishing, [2021] | Interest age level: 004-008. | Summary: A collection of humorous poetry that includes life
lessons, holiday-themed poems, animal stories, friendships,
and other mischief and shenanigans.
Identifiers: ISBN 9781737555605 (hardcover) | ISBN 9781737555612 (paperback) | ISBN 9781737555629 (ePub) | ISBN 9781737555636 (Kindle)
Subjects: LCSH: Animals--Juvenile poetry. | Pets--Juvenile poetry. | Friendship--Juvenile poetry. | Holidays--Juvenile poetry. | CYAC: Animals--Poetry.
| Pets--Poetry. | Friendship--Poetry. | Holidays--Poetry. | LCGFT: Humorous poetry. | Illustrated works.
Classification: LCC PZ7.1.P518 Wh 2021 (print) | LCC PZ7.1.P518 (ebook)
| DDC [E]--dc23

Library of Congress Control Number: 2021914265

Idle Brains Publishing
Chicago, IL

What's Wrong with a with a Pet Dinosaur?

Poems and Drawings
by Tony Philips

Idle Brains Publishing

To Cat
You asked
the question
that sparked
all this.

I Want the Very Best Birthday Party

First, we'll go sailing, then we'll go bowling
Then we'll play dodgeball to get this thing rolling,
Then we'll go skating and see a parade,
Then we'll eat ice cream outside in the shade.
All this will happen by half past eight.
Did you get all that down? If not, I can wait.
We'll go to the zoo then and see them feed bears,
And then we'll go tubing in trios and pairs.
We'll swim at the pool next, as long as it's sunny.
Why are you laughing? Did I say something funny?
Then we'll ride horses. Oh, my what a thrill!
Then we'll play ping pong and climb up a hill
Then a ball game next and take in a show.
Do you think all three hundred of my friends can go?
And we'll need some balloons
A few hundred will do
And at least a few clowns
And a magician or two
And forty-four pizzas
And don't forget–
Hey, where are you going?
We haven't discussed my cake yet.

The Tree House

I'm building a tree house, the finest indeed
I got all the lumber and tools that we'll need.
I got us a hammer and wood and some nails.
I got us some paint and some brushes and pails.
I got us some biscuits for lunch when we stop.
I got us some paper to cover the top.
I got us a window, a frame, and a door.
I got us some carpet to cover the floor.
I got us a sign with the words, "Keep out."
I got us a spyglass – you'll be the lookout.
I got us these things to make it real great.
I think we can build it before it gets late.
There's only one thing I didn't foresee:
Do you know, perhaps, where we can find us a tree?

Thanksgiving Pie

We'll have turkey and stuffing
And Brussel sprouts too.
Potatoes and cranberries,
And Aunt Ginny's stew.
Green beans and olives,
And a dip of fondue.
Some corn on the cob,
And a jar of cashews.
And bake them together
In a pumpkin pie.
There'll be nothing better.
Let's give it a try.

And if you won't taste it,
Just watch and you'll see.
My dad will eat anything
If it's made by me.

Piano Practice

I've been playing piano
For all of six minutes
I know that's not long
But the song's nearly finished.
Do you think I could stop now?
My hands really hurt.
I just want a snack,
Of some apple and yogurt.
And maybe I'll step out
To check out the sun
To see where it's gone
I'm sure that'd be fun!
And maybe I'll swing then
Or climb on the fence?
It'll help me relax
I feel really tense.
I can toss up a ball next
To work on my wrist.
My elbow's not working
I can't make a fist.
I think my two arms
Are not the same size.
If I hang from the bars,
That will help them align.
I can practice more later
You don't have to wait.
I'll be back before long
But don't fuss if I'm late.

Jeremy Meyer is Such a Liar

He says his brother once caught a gnome.
He says the tooth fairy stole his comb.
He says his dad's hair is made of foam.
Jeremy Meyer is such a liar.

He says there's a Leprechaun in the tree.
He says a witch put a spell on me.
He says his uncle taught his dog to ski.
Jeremy Meyer is such a liar.

He says there's a fairy that lives in his drawer.
He says his dad's name is Eleanor.
He says there's a mermaid who shops at the store.
Jeremy Meyer is such a liar.

He says his cousin has a carpet that flies.
He says his uncle has werewolf eyes.
He says his brother is a dog in disguise.
Jeremy Meyer is such a liar.

He says there's a troll in the wishing well.
He says he was born on a carousel.
He says he cracked the Liberty Bell.
Jeremy Meyer is such a liar.

He says his dad met his mom in jail.
He says his brother got stuck in a whale.
He says his aunt has a monkey tail.
Jeremy Meyer is such a liar.

He says his uncle has a ghost in a box.
He says his brother has a snake that talks.
He says there's a dragon that eats his socks.
Jeremy Meyer is such a liar.

I told him these things are all untrue.
I told him you can't grow grass on the moon.
Or fly a magic carpet to Timbuktu.
And crayons are not what makes blue cheese blue.
Now Jeremy is calling me a liar too!

But bluebirds aren't green, they are still blue.
The sky is not pink, nor is it maroon.
Some things are false, and others are true.
So let's shout from Maine to Kalamazoo.
(Can you help me out and shout the next line too?)
Jeremy Meyer is such a liar!

The Last Piece of Cake

One final piece of cake left.
A lonely sight to see.
One solitary piece of cake
A pastry tragedy.

We once had reams and reams of cake
With slices big and vast.
But one was gone, then more and more
And now we're at the last.

Do you intend to eat that cake?
That icing's much too sweet.
It doesn't look like anything
That you would want to eat.

I've heard it's bad to eat sweet cake
In morning and at night.
It might upset your insides
Then you won't feel quite
all right.

They say that cake is haunted,
With a ghost inside, you see.
That ghost, he tends to fight with you,
So you should let it be.

So maybe you should pass to me
That final piece of cake.
It's just to help you out, you know
And not get belly ache.

You say you'd like to share it?
Oh, that's great, that sounds
real swell.
There's just one little
problem:
That's the final fork
as well.

Kissing Frogs

I found a frog beside the road
And kissed him so he'd change.
He's still a frog. I'm not sure why.
I think it's kind of strange.
Another frog was in the pond.
I kissed him like a prince.
He didn't change. He's still a frog.
And hasn't croaked once since.
I think these frogs forgot about
The princes they once were.
I'm teaching them the royal life
So they can change to "sirs".
One more kiss, and if they change
We'll marry by the shore.
But if they don't, with one more kiss
I'll toss them back, no more!

I Need A Hug

I went to my gal and asked for a hug
"No way!" she said, it's true.
"You hurt me so bad the last time we met
There's no way I'm hugging you."

I told her I'd changed, I'd shed my old ways
"I'm not the same man you knew."
But she wouldn't get close, no hug for me
What's a porcupine to do?

Christmas Resolution

I knew all along this could happen someday.
That chimney looked small, but I tried anyway.
And I thought I could fit, but alas I could not.
So I'm stuck right now in a difficult spot.
But it left time to think, so think I did
Of things that I shouldn't or wouldn't or didn't.
Like, I shouldn't have eaten those last set of cakes
And the gingerbread cookies the other kid baked
And the snacks that girl left, but they were quite good.
Is that the sound of an axe chopping wood?
I should have done sit ups, like I promised last year
If I'd done so, perhaps then I wouldn't be here.
I'm a big man, you know, and no longer thin.
Is that smoke that I smell? There's an itch on my chin.
I should've taught the reindeer to call when I'm stuck
Then the elves could come lasso me out with their truck.
My shoulder feels numb and there's warmth by my feet.
It smells like some person is cooking some meat.
Oh dear! I think it's time for me to go!
Before Santa gets cooked by his plump Christmas toes.
I'll try to go back up the chimney this way.
But these fat clothes don't help, they just get in the way.
Please remember next year to help Santa out.
No more pop or cookies, only carrots and sprouts.
Once I'm out, I swear, I'm going straight to the gym.
Merry Christmas to all! Next year Santa will be thin!

The Giraffe's Fault

I was playing in the yard with my pet giraffe
He is fun and pretend and a laugh and a half
When he tipped the ladder with his big, long neck
And spilled the paint – the yard's a wreck
And the dog got wet and went berserk
And slipped his collar with one quick jerk
And jumped the fence to the neighbors' yard
And trampled on their garden hard
And tipped a vase and broke a vent
And kicked a pole which got all bent
And knocked the hose into the cellar
Which caused a mess for Mr. Gellar.
We tried to catch him but he just scat
And then he tried to chase the cat
Who shrieked and climbed way up the tree
Which bugged, I think, a bumble bee
And stung my brother on his knee.
Now everyone is blaming me.
But that was not my fault, you see.
Please tell my mother, if you agree.
It's the giraffe's fault, but she's mad at me.

Watch Your Step

Hey, hey you, yeah you, look over here!
Inside the mirror, it's me!
I'm not sure how I got in here.
But I need a way to flee.

I was walking backward the other day
And tripped and fell inside.
I don't know how to get back out.
Do you see a knob or slide?

It's kind of strange in this mirror world.
It's all backward left to right.
The door won't open and the window's stuck
And it's really cold at night.

You're the only person who's noticed me.
I'm so glad that you are there.
Can you please come and help me out
When you finish combing your hair?

Hey, hey, wait, hey wait, where are you going?
There are things you need to see.
We need to talk, we have so much in common
After all, you look just like me.

Don't Bring a Bear to Your Sister's Wedding

My sister said to bring one guest
I thought I'd bring a bear.
A bear is not a good guest to bring
But I was unaware.

The band started, and he hogged the dance floor
And didn't stop all night.
He ate the cake – every last bite
And gave the guests a fright.

They're not potty trained,
And they don't wear pants.
They won't bring a gift,
Only dance dance dance.

So if you want a blender
For your wedding day,
A bear's the wrong guest
In every which way.

The Snake's Legs

There once was a snake
With legs like a goose
Who had some big feet
And really big boots.
One day he got tired
Of walking around
And took his legs off
And laid himself down.
He took a short nap
And when he awoke
His legs were both gone.
Bootlegged by some bloke.
He looked and he looked
All upside and down
For those missing legs
All over the town.
But they were just lost
All places he looked
Like they had just slipped
Like a fish from a hook.
Without legs and arms
His body would slither
What else could he do
To get hither and thither.

He got good at sliding
And getting around
Just like you and me
All over the town.
So if there's a bloke
With goose legs and boots
You let the snake know
'Cause he's looking for those.

Jimmy Sand, the One-Man Band

I went to the dentist and got piano key teeth
And a banjo hand, in the space underneath
And a violin voice with four different strings
And a saxophone hand and a bell nose that rings
I'm my own marching band, you've gotta see me perform
The problem is my butt:
When it toots, it's a horn.

Personal Sun

I was tired of winter, so I ordered a sun
It's big and round and weighs a ton.
They dropped it off at my house last week.
It melted the snow almost instantly.
Then it melted the signs and it melted a tree.
And it melted the sidewalk and melted the street.
The neighbors are angry 'cause it burned up their yard.
They say it's too noisy and upsets their dog.
My mom says it's ugly and smells like a fart.
My dad complains he has no place to park.

But having your own sun has its pluses too.
It's the end of October and feels like June.
You can cook marshmallows whenever you like
And we can go swimming – even at night
There's never any snow, and hardly any rain.
Some people don't like it, but it's not such a pain.
It has no off switch, so it's always day.
When we want to sleep, we just close the shades.
There are problems, I guess, having a sun, it's true.
But if you could have your own sun, wouldn't you?

The Rabbit's Spaghetti

There once was a rabbit who cooked spaghetti,
The taste was so divine.
Everyone loved it, they couldn't get enough,
Even the pasta-hating swine.
The pig would eat it, only in secret,
And told the rabbit to never tell.
He did not want any others to know
He was a pasta-lover as well.

Every Sunday the pig would preach to others
What they shouldn't eat.
"Don't eat carrots, don't eat mangos,
Don't eat anything that's sweet."
He would stand on a box, proud and angry,
On the corner of the street,
And would always end his sermon thus:
"Don't eat spaghetti, I repeat!"

But in the dark of night, the pig would come,
Covered in a sheet,
Or disguised in a blanket and a hat,
Wearing horse's hooves for feet,
And would sit himself at the rabbit's bistro,
His favorite place to go,
And would feed himself on that angelic spaghetti,
Each time more and more, you know.

Then one day, a stray duck saw him
Putting spaghetti in his mouth.
And he quacked it up with his other friends,
And the horses started to shout.
"You're eating pasta," the horses said.
"You're doing what you told us don't."
The pig slurped a final noodle up.
"Don't do what I do," he groaned.

The horses didn't like that,
Nor the rabbit, nor the duck.
So they kicked him out of the bistro, and said,
"No more spaghetti for you, tough luck!"
Then one day the pig set his box on the corner,
And stepped up and began to speak.
"Spaghetti is the greatest food of all," he said,
"Please come, one and all, let's eat!"

Where Did I Come From?

You came from a place up near the North Pole
Where the bluebirds fly when it gets too cold.
You hatched from an egg that was left in the snow.
That's really where you came from.

No, really, really, where did I come from?

We found you in a box on a hill by a tree
Some bears left you there, some girl told me
We don't know why they left you, it's a mystery.
That's really where you came from.

No, really, really, where did I come from?

Your Dad cracked a walnut and you popped out.
You were purple and striped and had a small snout.
We cleaned you up and you started to sprout.
That's really where you came from.

No, really, really, where did I come from?

We found you in the bottom of a deep dark pit.
There were snakes and spiders and beetles that spit.
You were tied up in ribbons with shoes that didn't fit.
That's really where you came from.

No, really, really, where did I come from?

In a shady meadow where the pink grass grows
There's a quiet spot where the giant blows his nose.
You were in a green puddle without any clothes.
That's really where you came from.

No, really, really, where did I come from?

You came from a seed in your mamma's belly.
When you came out, you were quite smelly.
Your arms and legs were made of jelly.
That's really where you came from.

I'm tired of asking you for the truth
Your answers are silly and some are quite rude
I'll go ask my grandma, she knows more than you.
Grandma, where did I come from?

My Word

I'm going to make a word.
And that word will be mine.
No one else can use it
Til the end of time.

Don't sing it in a song.
Don't use it in a play.
Don't write it in a book.
Don't speak it anyway.

I'll lock it in a safe
And throw away the key,
Or keep it in a bank.
It's only there for me.

If I told you my word,
Can you give me one too?
Or maybe something else
Like a book or a shoe.

Or a house or a boat
Or a plane or a car.
Is it worth that much?
Oh yeah, by far.

What good is a word?
I'm surprised every day.
But I can't tell you –
That's the word I can't say.

The Salty Dessert

I add salt to my food
And salt to dessert.
I always say, a little bit of salt can't hurt.
I put salt on cupcakes
Salt on toast
Salt on fruitcake
Salt on roast
Salt on yogurt
Salt on gum
Salt on a melon
Salt on my thumb
My mom says it's sugar
That don't matter to me.
I still like that salt.
It tastes good, you see.

Vincent Vivendi

Vincent Vivendi is a broccoli head.
He eats in the tub and he drinks in his bed.
I told you before, and I'll say to the end,
Vincent Vivendi is not my friend.

He eats peas with a fork and spaghetti with a spoon.
He sleeps late on Mondays, and on Sundays till noon.
He won't color in the lines, and he can't play a tune.
Vincent Vivendi is such a buffoon.

He wears his hat backward, even at church.
He hid Mara's jacket, and then said, "Go search."
He put ketchup and mustard on top of ice cream.
Vincent Vivendi is not on my team.

He told my friend Clara that I was a goof.
Then he threw all the baseballs on top of the roof.
He put the cat in the mud and said she was clean.
Vincent Vivendi is the worst that I've seen.

He can't stay still and won't wash his hands.
He runs kind of funny and makes weird demands.
He sings as he walks and dances in line.
Vincent Vivendi is not one of mine.

Jan told me that he wears boots in bed.
Fran said that he put tape on her head.
There are so many things, that I have to report–
Oh, what did you say?
Did you say Vincent wants to be friends with me?
Oh, okay, yes, that will be fine.
We can be friends,
If he wants to be mine.

The Magic Bean

I once put a bean in my brother's nose
And I guess it was magic, 'cause it sprouted and rose
In a day and half, a vine spiraled up.
It soon touched the clouds, and then somehow got stuck.

We yanked and we yanked, but it wouldn't release.
It lifted my brother up right off his feet!
He was dangling there, so I decided to climb up
To see what I could do to get him unstuck.

What I found at the top was a stubborn old duck
Who was parked on that vine, and would not give it up.
I asked him to leave, I even said please.
But the duck wouldn't listen, he just quacked at me.

I wondered what to do to unseat this sour duck
To get him to move and undo this bad luck.
I offered him candy, I offered him tea.
But the duck merely sat there, quacking at me

Then a plane flew by,
It was strangely off course.
I looked at the pilot,
He had the head of a horse!
I asked the duck nicely,
I got on my knees.
But the duck merely snorted
And would not agree.

I offered him peanuts, I offered him toast.
I offered him walnuts, my shirt and my clothes.
I offered to take him to the pond with my niece
And the circus to see the flying trapeze.

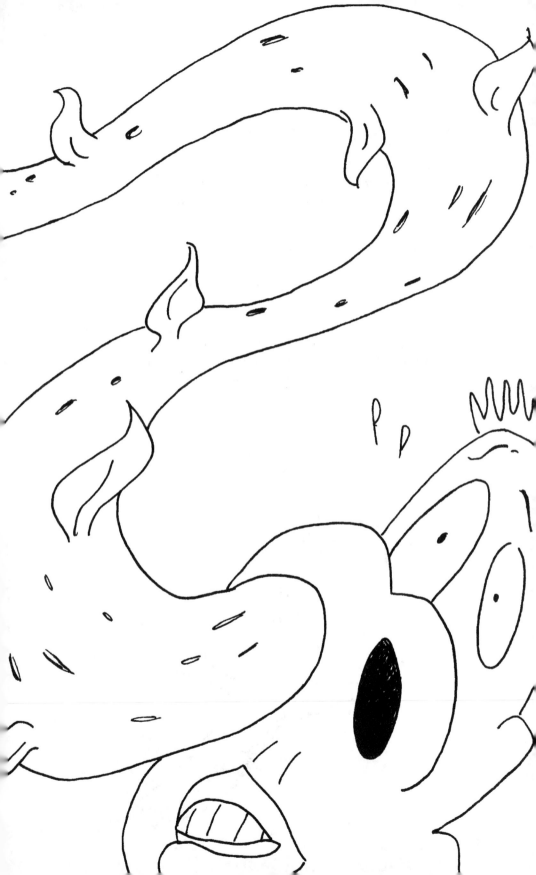

But the duck wouldn't listen, he sat like a stone
I worried for my brother, far far below.
I asked him, "Dear duck, is there something you seek?
Is there something you want in exchange, pretty please?"
The duck looked at me, and then quacked out a tweet.
It was simply two words, what he said was: "Your feet."

So, we traded our feet and we traded a nose.
I know this sounds strange, but that's how it goes.
And that's how I came to have two duck feet
And a duck bill in front instead of my teeth.

So, if you see a strange duck with my feet walking 'round
With my pearly white smile when you're shopping in town,
Please let me know, 'cause I still want my teeth,
It turns out you can't eat spaghetti with a beak!

What's Wrong
with a Pet Dinosaur?

I used to have a pet dinosaur.
He was big and he was brown.
At night when he laid down to sleep
It felt like the house might fall down.
When he snored sometimes the windows broke.
And if he farted, you couldn't breathe.
But he was always my favorite pet.
I don't know why Mom made him leave.

What Comes After Z?

At school, Miss Marks taught us
One, two, and three,
A, B and C,
And then O through Z.
I know N follows M,
And Q follows P,
But the puzzle I see
Is not H, J, or G,
It is, what is the letter
That comes after Z?

I asked Miss Marks,
But she gave me a frown,
"There're 26 letters,
You can ask the whole town.
There're no more letters,
After X, Y and Z.
Just ask anyone,
They'll tell you, you'll see."

But something's not right
In that answer, I thought.
Something that irked me
And pained me a lot.
26 letters aren't enough
To make all the words
That I knew, so I thought.

I've been to the aquarium
And there're fishes galore.
26 couldn't name
Just the ones in the store.
I've counted all the words
And there are far too many,
Like eggplant and gopher
and walrus and penny.

I've seen all the books
Up in grandpa's study.
They are dusty and old
And they smell kind of funny.
But each of those books
Has too many words.
26 aren't enough,
For all the books in the world.

So I asked the old lady
Who stands by the fence,
And the man at the grocery
With polka dot pants,
And the man at the gas station
Who speaks kind of funny,
And the girl at the bank
Who handles the money.

But none of them knew.
They all scrunched up their faces.
It was like I put poo
On their plate at the races.
They didn't want to answer
My question at all.
It was like I was screaming,
Like that man at the mall.

So I was sad and confused
And kind of befuddled.
How could it be
This was so much trouble?
I just wanted to know
What comes after Z?
It's not like I was asking
The square root of nineteen.

Then a big, blue person
In stockings and cap
Appeared at our doorstep,
With a bag and a flap.
It was the mail lady, I knew,
Who brings us our mail.
"No packages today," she waved,
With blue fingernails.

So I asked her my question,
What harm could it do?
They all thought I was crazy,
As crazy as a moo.

But she didn't frown,
And she didn't shake.
She didn't wave me away
With a broom and a rake.

She laughed instead,
And made a half-smile.
"That's silly, ol' miss," she said,
"It's been 'crocodile' for awhile."

"I thought it might be,"
I leapt to my feet.
And jumped off my perch
And ran down the street.

Finally, finally, someone told me
The secret letter that comes after Z.
I had to tell Emma
And that girl they call Bea,
And the girl who makes cakes
With her toes by the lake.

There aren't 26 letters
I know that's true now.
There are animal letters and more than just cow.
From bluebird to dolphin to monkey and fish
I've counted twenty-two, but don't think that's it.

If you know more letters.
Please tell me them now.
Put your face by the page
And whisper them aloud.

I'll hear them somehow,
Somehow I'm sure.
26 aren't enough,
For all the words in the world.

The Great Machine

I am going to build a great machine
The greatest machine you've ever seen.

It'll make lemon ice cream
From old paper bags.
It will have eleven arms
And seventeen legs.

It'll be made of lightning
And old kite string.
It'll be the biggest thing
That you've ever seen!

It'll be quicker than a cheetah
And stronger than an ox.
It will always be silent
And listen when you talk.

It will have spinning
wheels
And rotating frogs
It will be made of
cupcakes
And old Lincoln logs.

It'll be lighter than a
feather
And fold really small.
It will fit in your pocket
And grow super tall.

It will tell that kid Micky
To stay in his place.
It will be faster than Rodney
When they run the race.

It will look like a kid
    With a robot head.
        It will guard me at school.
        And sleep in my bed.

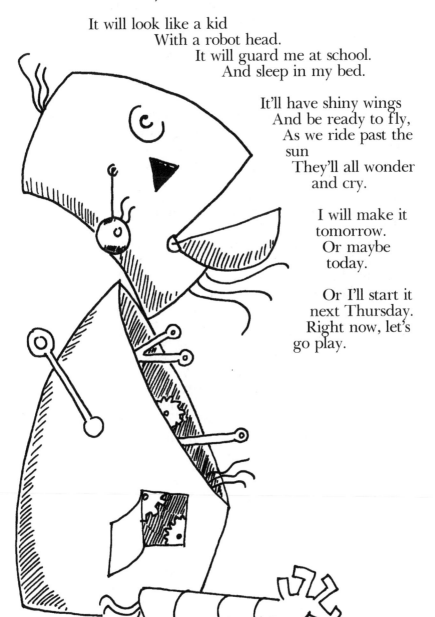

It'll have shiny wings
    And be ready to fly,
    As we ride past the
    sun
        They'll all wonder
        and cry.

I will make it
tomorrow.
    Or maybe
    today.

Or I'll start it
next Thursday.
Right now, let's
go play.

The Penguin Who Couldn't Swim

There once was a penguin who didn't want to swim.
He didn't like the water, he wouldn't go in.
Other penguins were surprised, and some were concerned.
Why this young penguin did not want to learn.
"It's fun," they said. "Swimming's a treat.
Just jump in the water with both of your feet."
"I don't want to get wet," he shook his head.
It didn't matter what the other penguins said.
He wasn't going to swim. He was not going in.
Instead, he would fly with those two flappy fins.
"You can't fly with those fins," they said. "They're not strong."
"Just jump in the water. We'll all get along."
"I don't want to," he waved. "I'm going to fly
One day, you'll see me up there in the sky."
So he climbed up a hill, to get a bit higher.
He thought that would help him achieve his desire.
But the snow there was melting, it couldn't freeze.
And he sank in the slush to the top of his knees.
So he kicked in the slush, and his wings, he flapped.
But he only sank more in the snow after that.
"Oh dear," he sighed. "How am I going to fly
Like the giant squids that swoop in the sky?"
"Giant squids don't fly," said his friend Marguerite,
Who had followed him there with her two penguin feet.
"Those are birds," she told him. "Squids only swim."
"I'm a bird," said the penguin, who was sunk to his fins.
"That's true," she agreed. "But you're going down."
"Alas," he said, as he sank in the ground.
Then his head went under, and he kicked with his feet.
And he found he could swim, in the sea underneath.
And he swam real fast, faster than most.
He needed to swim to the edge of the coast.

When he reached the coast, he was going quite fast.
His friends were bewildered as he zoomed right past.
And he swam straight up, up up to the sky.
Other penguins noticed and wondered why.
And he burst through the water and flew in the air.
It was only a few feet, but so what, he was there.
"I did it! I did it! I flew with my feet,
With the fins the world gave me, I flew, did you see?"
And they saw that he did,
And they clapped for their friend.
Who knew a penguin could fly?
But he did, in the end.

The Spicy Carrot

My sister warned the carrot was spicy.
I didn't heed her advice
I thought, how bad can it possibly be?
Two bites, then I knew the price.

"It's burning!" I shouted. My mouth was on fire.
Flames were inside of my head.
I realized if this continued any longer,
I'd probably soon be dead!

"Water!" she shouted. We went to the sink.
I drank a gallon or more.
The water was sloshing around in my gut.
But the burning was the same as before.

"Milk!" she said and poured me a glass.
I drank it and made a loud slurp.
But still, I felt I was breathing fire
Each time I made a burp.

"Peanuts," she said and fed me a bunch.
They went down without even a chew
I looked surprised, but my sister said.
"Don't worry, they'll pass in your poo."

"Bread," she said. "That'll soak up the carrot."
I'm not sure that's even true.
But I ate the bread, with some peanut butter.
"But no jelly," she said. "That won't do."

"Still burning?" she asked. My lips were all numb.
I spoke, but my mouth was all gummy.
That spicy carrot was not good to eat.
It was at war, it seemed, with my tummy.

"Try ice," she said. So I ate some cubes.
They sizzled like steak on a grill.
My throat was broiled and my tongue was seared.
But the ice finally let me sit still.

So, I keep eating ice, all the time, every day.
An inferno still burns in my guts.
They say it'll stop. Meantime, I just wait.
Man, eating that carrot was nuts!

Watermelon Seed

My mom swallowed a seed.
It's growing in her belly.
They say it's a baby
I think it's a melon.
I saw her swallow it
At the picnic last summer.
Won't everyone be surprised,
When it's a fruit, not a brother!

Big

My feet are too big for my shoes now.
My neck doesn't fit through my shirt.
My arms are too long for my sleeves now.
My pants are so tight they hurt.

My socks barely cover my ankles.
My hat doesn't fit on my lid.
My mom says I need to stop growing.
Or I'll be too big for a kid!

The Pig Who Wouldn't Bathe

There once was a pig who was quite a stink.
He refused to ever clean.
The neighbors complained he reeked so much
It made their pets turn green.

His stench could turn fresh milk to sour
And strip the walls of paint.
It'd burn your eyes, and scratch your throat
And cause most kids to faint.

So the neighbors told him it was time to wash
But the pig simply refused.
He said, "I've got no time for that."
And sprayed on skunk perfume.

The neighbors couldn't stand the smell
They said, "That's much too stink."
So they dunked him in the frothy ocean
And scrubbed him in a sink.

And they told him to wash, or they'd do it again.
So the pig, he had to change.
And he started to shower, and sing as he did,
And what happened next was strange.

His singing was beautiful, and everyone loved it!
He was adored because he could sing.
And all because he was forced to wash.
See, there's a reason for everything!

Finnegan Bleck

Finnegan Bleck
Had a bug in his neck
"I was riding the swing,
And I started to sing,
And it flew in my mouth,
And it didn't come out!"

So, he went to the doctor
And the doctor said.
"Finnegan dear,
I want to be clear,
That bug in your neck,
That bug that you saw,
Is not in your neck,
It's not there at all."

But Finnegan Bleck
Could not accept.
"It is in my neck.
It is there indeed.
I will prove it to you.
And to you. You will see."

But how? he thought.
And poor Finnegan didn't know.
So he consulted his sister.
Who knew these things so.

"Try jumping," she said.
So Finnegan jumped,
He jumped up and down.
To shake that bug out.
He jumped thirty-three times.
And then ten, but lost count.

When that didn't work,
She said, "Drink." So he drank.
Eighty glasses of water.
And a lime which was sour.
But it only made Finnegan
Need to pee every hour.

"Stand on your head," she said.
So he stood upside-down
For eighty-eight minutes
On top of his crown
But that bug didn't budge.
That's what Finnegan found.

"I need something else," he said.
"Something that works."
"Try to freeze it out," she said.
As she waved with a fork.
She was reading a book
For her third-grade homework.

So he ate eighty scoops
Of vanilla ice-cream
All covered in chocolate.
In a bowl he licked clean.

But no matter what he ate
Of ice cream and fudge.
That bug in his neck,
It would not budge.

"Did you swallow?" she asked.
"Yes," he said, "But that bug.
Is still stuck in my neck.
Like a stain on a rug."

"It is a peculiar bug," she said.
"Quite stubborn and sticky.
I think you should try
Something smooth and quite
Icky."

So he ate some worms
And spiders and flies.
(These were, of course,
Of the gummy kind.)

And raindrops and gumdrops
And ickleberry pies.
But no matter how much,
That bug would not flee.
It was stuck in his neck
Like a cat in a tree.

"I give up," said his sister,
"I think it's too much."
She closed her book
And gave him a shrug.

"That bug isn't moving.
It's stuck like a plug.
You'll have to accept.
Now you're Finnegan Bug.

58

"No, I'm not!" he said
But he knew it was so.
There was no more to do
And he felt he should go.

So dejected and sad,
He went to the park.
But the swings were all wet.
So he hung from the bars.
And he felt a small bubble
Inside of his chest.
And a burp came out.
You can imagine the rest.
The bug flew from his mouth.
He was rid of that pest!

"Goodbye, bug!" he said.
"It's almost sad to see you go.
I was looking forward to some
More pickles in snow!
And riding a donkey
And climbing a bus
And doing more things
That are wrong, but so what?
I got rid of that bug,
That's all that matters, I'm sure.
It's a miracle after all,
A burp is the cure!"

Too Many
Blueberry Pies

My momma likes baking
Blueberry pies.
She bakes many shapes
Of big and small size.

They're piled to the ceiling
On the fridge and the floor.
Sometimes she stacks them
On top of the door.

On top of the toilet,
On top of the sink,
Blueberry pies
Everywhere you could
think.

Why does she
bake them?
She still won't say.
She just keeps
baking them
Night and
day.

I can't eat
any more
Blueberry pies.
My skin's
turning blue.
Can you
maybe
guess why?

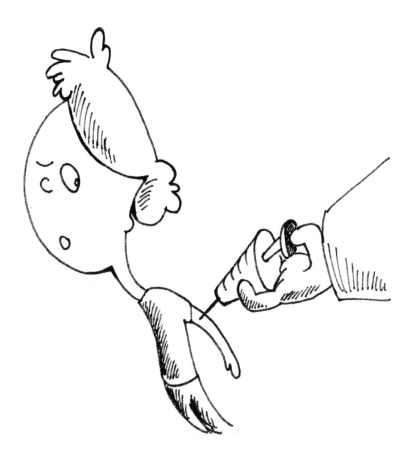

Got a Shot

The doctor says I need a shot
I don't like that at all
She says it doesn't hurt too much.
But I'm petite and small.
My arm will hurt, I'm sure of that.
I'll likely need a sling.
I'll struggle just to write my name
Or do most anything.
Oh why oh why oh why oh why
Do I have to get a shot?
If you gave me any other choice,
I'd simply rather not!

No way, no way, what's that you say?
I got it? It's over? I'm done?
Why'd you make such a big fuss about that?
It didn't hurt none.

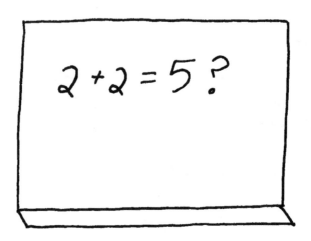

The Pig and the Calculator

There once was a pig who was more than a mess
He hadn't a pencil or a lace or a vest
But he could solve equations, even hard ones too
With a calculator that he hid in his shoe.

"18 times 80," said the rabbit. "And then add nine."
The pig had the answer in almost no time.
"One thousand four hundred and, I think, forty nine,"
He said as he munched on some swill like a swine.

"Ninety minus eighty," said
the horse, munching hay.
"Ten," said the pig.
"That wasn't hard in
any way."
"A million minus
one," said the
mouse by the
door.
"Nine hundred
ninety nine," said
the pig. "E minus 4?"

"That's wrong,"
said the rabbit, as
he leaned on the
device.
The pig squealed
loud as the screen
shattered twice.
"Oh no," said the pig.
"I can't add without
that!"
"Use your brain," said
the rabbit. "The device
in your hat!"

The Big Sneeze

I sneezed so hard
I went back in time.
And landed in yesterday,
One day behind.

Do you know where today is?
That's where I belong.
I want to get back there
Before it's too long.

I heard that the hiccups
Might do the work.
So I drank fizzy drinks,
But they just made me burp.

They say if you're busy,
That time will just fly.
So I got real busy
Making mulberry pies.

But I made so much pie,
You could feed a whole fleet.
And the day was still yesterday–
Just one more defeat.

They say if you sleep,
Tomorrow will come.
So I slept really long,
And then more and then
some

But when I awoke,
I noticed with dread,
The day was still yesterday.
So right back to bed.

I heard if you run,
It will speed up your time,
So I ran really fast,
For an hour and nine.

And I ran all the way
To the next town and then,
But it wasn't tomorrow,
So I turned back again.

I started to think
Tomorrow won't come.
I'll be stuck back in yesterday
For forever and some.

And that made me glum
And I wanted to cry,
But I won't let that stop me
I needed to try.

To get to tomorrow
I'll need to be bright

I'll need to be clever
I'll need to sit tight.

I'll stay up all night
And at the last second,
I'll jump really hard,
To tomorrow, I reckon.

'Cause they say if you jump
When the night bleeds to gray,
You might see tomorrow
Before it's today!

The Audition

I've got thirty-two minutes to learn a new song.
I'm worried and scared that I might sing it wrong.
It's my first audition and I want to get it right.
I want to blast my voice to the box seats tonight.

There're twenty-four minutes, since I wrote
that last line.
But I can still do this, there's plenty of time.
I just need to learn this brilliant new song.
I'll get it all right and sing it real strong.

There're eighteen minutes so I need to focus.
I wish I knew some hocus-pocus
To learn this song in the blink of an eye.
Opening night is in late July.

Ten minutes now and I'm starting to worry.
I think I can still learn this song in a hurry.
The pages and notes are looking quite blurry.
I'll study them now and learn it all in a flurry.

There're five minutes left so I'm going to start.
I really hope that I can get this part.
If I don't get this part, I hope you agree,
At least you got this – a nice poem from me.

Summer Christmas

Dear Santa,
I know that you're busy, but I need a favor.
I'm starting a new project, and it needs some labor.
Can you spare a few elves? I need a whole crew.
It would help me out. There's so much to do!
And I need a sleigh, a big one preferred,
And some flying reindeers, enough for a herd.
And I need a fur coat and a beard that is white.
One just like yours would be quite all right.
And I need a big sack that holds thousands of toys.
And a copy of the list of the good girls and boys.
I need this tomorrow, is that okay?
If you need more time, I can wait one more day.
I'm starting a new holiday, it's crazy, I know.
It's called Summer Christmas, and it won't involve snow.
It won't be in December, it will be in June.
The kids will all get gifts, in one afternoon.
But two Christmases would be hard for one guy.
So I thought I'd help out, could we give it a try?
Two Christmases will be double the fun.
Two Christmases will be better than one.
Let me know, Santa, as soon as you might.
I'd like to start practicing with the reindeer tonight!

Who Left the Toilet Seat Up?

Everyone is always blaming me.
But it's not my fault this time, you see.
I have three older sisters, any of these
Could've left the toilet seat up.

We have to share the bathroom as a matter of course.
But I'd rather share it with a pig and a horse.
It's busy with sisters from eight until three
There's rarely a moment for someone like me.

I need to go just like anyone else.
I need some time just to sit by myself.
They're always knocking, "Please, let me in!"
They've kicked me out before I can begin!

They're always complaining I take too long.
They're always saying it stinks when I'm gone.
But I'm only a boy, it's unfair to be
Blocked from the bathroom if I just need to pee!

Now they're knocking and shouting, while I write this for you.
There's a new mystery, and what should I do?
I'm at a loss right now to explain this feat,
But someone has stolen the toilet seat!

Always Eat the Icing First

I always eat the icing first.
It's the best part of the cake.
The icing is the first to go.
I do not want to wait.

Sometimes it's best to bite it off.
Or lick it from your plate.
Or poke it with your little finger
Or scrape it like a rake.

Once the icing's gone, there's only cake.
Which is not so nice to see.
I don't like cake without the icing.
Cake alone is not for me.

"Why don't you eat cake?" my momma asks,
"You leave it on your plate."
"Once the icing's gone, no thank you," I say.
"The icing makes it great."

"I'd eat icing on toast," I say. She looks surprised.
"And on noodles and eggplant and rice
I'd put icing on kale and beans and carrots
And eat it, I wouldn't think twice."

"Would you eat icing on ham?" my momma asks.
"Or on broccoli or spinach or peas?
You rarely eat those foods at all."
I say, "Pass the icing please."

"I'd put icing on pizza, chicken, and steak,
On meatloaf, and in a pie.
Icing is the best food of all.
There's nothing better, don't even try."

So now I eat all my vegetables
And other foods my momma favors,
Because she adds some icing on top
To match my favorite flavor.

The Duck Who Wished
He Was a Falcon

There once was a duck, a strange, odd duck,
Who wished he was a falcon,
He crafted big wings and fake sharp claws
And on his feet they mounted.
And he climbed a mountain up up high
To see if he could soar,
So he could see the world much like
A falcon did before.

But the wings didn't work too well at all
And he crashed into a tree.
He was stuck in there for many hours,
Until along came a bee.
"Are you a duck?" the bee asked, wondering.
"I notice you have claws."
"No, I'm a falcon," said the duck, unsure.
"I just stopped in here to pause."

"You don't look like a falcon," said the bee,
Who was buzzing in a way.
That's when the duck saw the bee's odd nose,
Elongated and gray.
"Are you a bee?" asked the duck, wondering aloud
About this curious bee.
"No," said the bee. "I'm an elephant.
And you need to leave my tree."

"Elephants don't live in trees," said the duck,
Not sure here what was true.
"And falcons don't have duck bills," said the bee.
"Now, move on, it's time to shoo."
So, the duck climbed down, his wings and claws
Still stuck up in the tree.
And the bee put them on, wings and claws, and said,
"I'm a falcon now, yippee!"

Monster Under the Bed

They say there's no monster
Under my bed.
But I know better.
He's in the closet instead.
He likes to eat kids.
I'm sure that's a shock.
I keep my door closed.
I keep my door locked.
One day he'll get out.
And we'll finally meet.
That's why I keep candy
Under my sheet.
Because candy is better –
Kids aren't that sweet.
Who would want kids
If there're gummies to eat?
So that's my whole plan.
It may not be shrewd.
I'll try to use candy
To avoid being food.

Sticky Fingers

There're handprints on the TV
And the counter, it's not clean.
There're white marks on the windows
And some goo stuck on the screen.
There're prints left on the doorknob
And some gunk left on the sink.
We want to find who did this,
But it's harder than you think.
I'm busy eating honey
And gluing glitter to my shoe.
If you find the one who did this,
Tell my mom, she's asking too.

I Have to Toot

I have to toot
It hurts to hold it in.
But if you toot in church
I think it's a sin.

So I keep it in
As far as that goes.
But when they sing loud
I let the wind blow.

One time they were singing
It just couldn't wait.
I let out some breeze.
It felt really great.

But they paused in their song.
As I let out that air.
And everyone heard it.
That ended the prayer.

And everyone laughed
All over the place.
Except for my mom
Who turned red in the face.

So my mom told me
Don't toot in church.
I have to hold it in
Even if it hurts.

But other people laughed
They didn't seem to mind.
It's not such a bad thing
It seems, all the time.

So I'm waiting right now
For the choir to hoot.
So I can relax
And let out my toot.

Stephanie Daisy is Much Too Lazy

She won't pick up her clothes,
Because they're close to the floor.
She won't hang her jacket,
Because it's far from the door.

She won't walk the dog,
Because he's starting to smell.
She won't feed the turtle,
Because he's got a big shell.

She won't set the table,
Because the napkins won't fold.
She won't wipe her mouth,
Because it makes her lips cold.

She won't wash her elbows,
Because they bend in the middle.
She won't eat her peas,
Because they're too round and little.

She won't wash the dishes,
Because it bothers her skin.
She won't flush the toilet,
She's afraid of falling in.

She won't take a bath,
Because she'll get too wet.
She won't take a shower,
She's not tall enough yet.

She won't wash her ears,
Because they're close to her head.
She won't brush her teeth,
If she's already in bed.

She won't dress herself,
Because it's too much trouble.
She won't use shampoo,
Because there're too many bubbles.

She won't say, "Thank you"
Because it bothers her tongue.
She won't say, "Please"
Because it squeezes her lung.

And she won't say goodnight,
Because she doesn't have time.
And she won't read my poems,
Because there're too many rhymes.

Oh My God, Oh My God, We Elected McPutty!

Oh my god, oh my god, we elected McPutty!
Can you imagine anyone – anyone – more nutty?
McPutty! McPutty! He is the worst!
We couldn't be more wrong, this is a first!

McPutty wants catsup to be our school drink.
McPutty wants to remove all the toilets and sinks.
McPutty wants to send all the girls out of town.
McPutty wants to ban any brownies that aren't brown.
McPutty wants lasagna for our lunch every week.
McPutty wants our language to be ancient Greek.
McPutty wants to ban sports to make us feel worse.
McPutty says the school has been afflicted with a curse.
McPutty says our problems are from ghosts in the air.
McPutty says that kids should wear tight underwear.

McPutty has no solutions, he blames other things.
The problem is McPutty and the songs that he sings.
Oh, what shall we do with McPutty's next bit?
I'm sorry, I think I might throw up after it.

Aunt Becky's Husband Has Big Ears

Aunt Becky's husband has big ears.
Too big for his head, to all that's clear.
One's a bit higher, and they're not the same size.
And they don't seem to line up correct with his eyes.
I like him a lot, don't get me wrong.
And his hearing is fine, if not too strong.
But what's with those ears? They're like big flappy wings.
Maybe one day he'll fly off with those things!
And his nose seems fake, like it's tied to his head.
And his hair is a wig – there's a stand by his bed.
It's a disguise he glues each day in place.
I want to be there when he takes off that face!

Who Ate All the Sugar in the Sugar Bowl?

Who ate all the sugar in the sugar bowl?
It wasn't me, that's all I know.
It could be the dog
Or the cat, let's see.
Or it could be my sister.
She likes her sweets.
Or it could be the mailman.
Or the neighbor next
door.
He likes to eat candy.
While he cleans the
floor.
Or it could be my
dad.
He has a sweet
tooth.
Or it could be
my mom.
She's
suspicious, it's
true.
I'm not a detective,
So I don't know who.
Okay, I ate a little.
But those others
Did too.

Unicorn for Christmas

For Christmas, I wished for a real unicorn.
I wanted one with a shiny gold horn.
With white ears and freckles and big green teeth
And a ring of posies to wear as a wreath.

The one that came was really small.
He's only three and a half inches tall.
I asked if he'll get bigger.
My parents said no.
They said that's the biggest size
He'll ever grow.

He's made of cement
And silly putty.
I don't think this is
Really that funny.
A big unicorn
That is what I asked for
Instead, I got a toy
That just sits on the floor.

So I'm writing you, Santa,
Because you should know
To leave better stuff than this
Where you go!

Next year, there might not be cookies for you.
And no glass of steamed milk with cinnamon too!

If you fix this, then we can forget this hubbub.
Otherwise, I'd say, you've made quite a flub.

My friend Susie got a puppy.
My friend Emma got a doll.
That doesn't seem very fair at all.

I'm letting you know, Santa, that you can do more.
I want a real unicorn – the kind I adore!

What do Pets do When
Their Owners are Away?

What do pets do when their owners are away?
Do they have a party? Do they put on a play?
I was wondering that thing, so I stayed once and hid.
I could not believe what I saw that they did.
The dog rode a bicycle and the cat wore your skates
And the parakeet chased them while spinning two plates!
The rabbit raided the fridge and ate all the plums.
Then he planted some seeds, he has a green thumb!

The dog tipped the vase and it fell on the cat.
And the rabbit ate the leaves and the parakeet laughed.
And the cat, in his mood, took a bath in the sink.
And the rabbit brought a towel, then they had a hot drink.
The dog baked a cake, he knows how to cook!
And he made brownies too from a recipe book!
And the parakeet ate them, along with a peach.
And the cat juggled lemons, and then gave a speech!
I wish I had a photo to prove it all to you.
Because the dog broke the vase. You doubt it, but it's true.

Oliver Grundy and the Footprints

Oliver Grundy
On alternate Sundays
Would follow the imprints
Of other people's footprints.

"I wish to expose
The owner of these toes,
Because he leaves a mess
Everywhere he steps."

So raining or snowing
Oliver was going
In fierce pursuit
Of some infamous boots.

Then one day in May
His friend Sandy did say,
"Hey, Oliver dear,
It's sunny and clear.
Let's go out and play
In the playground this way."

"No, I can't go play,"
Said Oliver dismayed,
"Nor the following Monday.
Nor the Tuesday past Sunday.
I must chase these clues
To the owner of these shoes."

So he traced that track
Through his yard and out back
And it led him around
Through the fields and the town
Then back to his door
To his shoes on the floor.

"Holy boots!" he exclaimed.
"Am I to be shamed?
Can it truly be
That these prints lead to me?"

"Oh, Oliver, dear,"
His mother appeared
"It's been that way
From the very first day.
Now go up and wash,
You're a mess, oh my gosh!"

So Oliver Grundy
The very next Sunday
Left his boots by the door
And never did more
Tramp in the imprints
Of other people's footprints.

Treasure Time

Hey, I found a treasure chest!
There're things inside, I'm sure.
I found it in our momma's bedroom,
Resting on the floor.
We need to crack it open,
Yes, I said that, you and I.
Can you go get the hammer now,
As I begin to pry?
I think we'll get it open soon,
With luck, so let us try.
The lock is old, and we are bold,
Please don't keep asking why.
Let's throw it down the staircase.
That should probably make it crack.
We need to test this now or else
Momma will soon be back!
It sounds like gold and jewels inside,
I'll bet my lucky dime.
We need to work, chop, chop, let's go,
Come on, it's treasure time!

Best-Dressed Fox

We once had a fox who seemed quite confused.
He dressed in a bow tie and black patent shoes.
And carried a briefcase and wore argyle socks.
It made you wonder if he forgot what he's not!
Then one day Aunt Gina paid a visit in May
And saw that fox dressed in his unique way.
She took to him instantly, it was love at first sight
And they drove to Las Vegas and were married that night!
We tried to tell Gina he's a fox, not a man.
She said, "I can't tell the difference, so *what* if you can?
He's the best-dressed fellow that I've ever met.
What does it matter if he's a man or pet?"
So they moved to Dallas and been together for years
And they have three kids with those big pointy ears
And he has a good job and they're all quite impressed.
It turns out a fox as a husband is best!

Baboon Face

I was always a very expressive child
And often made faces so crazy and wild.
My momma did warn me if I acted that way,
My face would get stuck in that look then someday.

And so it did, one winter morning,
When my brother was being as usual – annoying.
And I made a face like a howling baboon
And my face got all stuck just that way, no, it's true.

I couldn't believe it, nor could my ma.
So, she called up the doctor, who said, "Hey, what's wrong?"
And she said I had taken the face of a baboon,
And the doctor said, you better come over here soon.

The doctor was surprised, so he ran some tests.
But I couldn't change my face, though I tried my best.
He couldn't decide just what might be wrong.
So we saw a specialist, Dr. WhatZingGo Fong.

WhatZingGo's office was right by the zoo.
So we took a detour and saw a zebra or two.
Then WhatZingGo saw me and knew really quick
What was causing my problem – it was an IckBillyIck.

"An IckBillyIck?," ma said, "Is there such a thing?"
"It's true," said WhatZingGo, as he tied up some string.
"The IckBillyIck mostly lives in your tummy.
But if it gets loose, your face freezes funny."

"So, what do we do?" asked my ma, quite concerned.
"We go to the zoo," said the doctor, in turn.
We'll start at the baboon cage, and then go from there.
If that doesn't solve it, then we'll try the bears."

"Are you a real doctor?" my ma cried out loud.
"Yes," said the Fong. "And we must hurry now."

When we got to the baboons, they were sleepy it looked.
Only one of them was moving. He was reading a book.
"Do baboons read?" I asked, confused and befuddled.
"Ask your dad," ma said. "Now what's next?" she mumbled

Then the baboon saw me and became quite engaged.
He ran up real close, right up to the cage.
And he howled real loud, showing teeth in his cheeks.
In the back of my throat, I heard a loud squeak.

Then my face felt relaxed, no longer so stuck.
My momma turned white, but then signaled thumbs up.
"The IckBillyIck," Fong said, "Can be scared.
If you frighten it, then it'll flee back down there."

So now I don't make faces like I once did.
I don't want to upset the IckBillyIck.
When my brother's annoying, I try to just smile.
If my face freezes up, it'll be a grin for a while.

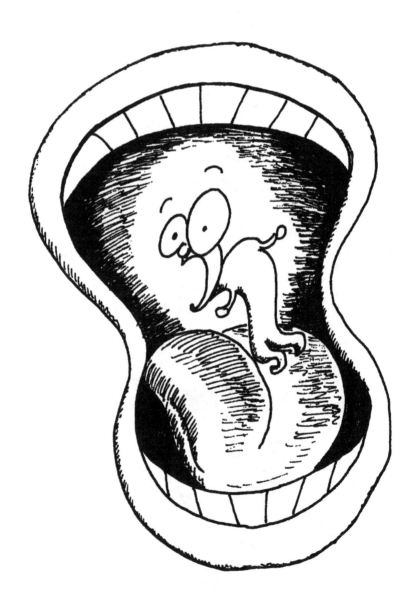

The Lemonade Stand

We need to raise two hundred dollars
For the winter school field trip.
So we built a lemonade stand
To try to earn a bit.
Do you want a lemonade?
It's good, I'll pour you one real quick.
It doesn't cost too much at all.
Just two hundred dollars, that's it.

Captain Cluck, the Floating Duck

There once was a duck who claimed he could hover
Up in the air with no tricks to discover.
And he made us all pay a penny to see
Him perform that feat in barn number three.

He climbed on the stage, which was really a board,
And proceeded to float away from the floor.
And turned upside down and remained in the air,
And no one could see anything holding him there.

"How do you do that?" the chicken inquired.
Of asking questions, she and the horse never tired.
"Ducks don't tell secrets," quipped the duck upside down.
"I just decided not to stick to the ground."

"There must be a trick," the horse flicked an ear.
"Otherwise, all of us would be there and not here."
"I know the trick," claimed the rabbit in gray.
He nibbled a carrot, his choice for the day.

"He put cheese on his feet and then stuck to a spot,
And that's why he's there, and we all are not."
"There's no cheese," quacked the duck, as he stepped on
a beam.
"Cheese I would eat. It was pistachio ice cream."

Then the animals all laughed and clapped in their stalls.
Then stepped in the ice cream and tramped on the walls.

Do you Want a Womp?

There's a womp in my kitchen. I wish he would leave.
He eats so much food you wouldn't believe!
I told him to go, I told him to shoo.
He didn't like that, and then there were two!
Two womps are even more worse than one.
On Thursday alone, they ate all my buns.
And four hundred candies and seven whole cakes.
They drank all my milk, but no bellyaches!
I told them to stop, I said they can't stay.
They didn't like that. There were three the next day!
The three ate my yogurt and all of my meat.
They breathe really hard and smell like old feet.
They emptied the freezer, they ate all the flour.
They ate all the sugar, and more every hour!
They drank all the soda and burped half the day.
When they're not eating, they get in the way.
I once stepped on one, he let out a roar.
I told him to stop, and then there were four!

Do you want a womp? I can spare at least two.
But don't try to tell them a thing they can't do!

Stop Following Me

I told you this yesterday
But you don't seem to see
Following me everywhere
Is as weird as can be.

I find it quite creepy
How you glide over walls
And cling to my feet
And get big and then small.

And you always put me
Between you and the light.
It's like you can't tolerate
The sun when it's bright.

You're not my best friend
And you're sure not my mate.
I don't need you following me
From dawn until late.

These things are never easy
It's sure hard to hear.
"It's not you, it's me, friend.
Now please disappear!"

There're other people out there
Who need shadows too.
You can be their shadow
Just not mine, we're through.

They say a person's shadow
Glues their feet to the ground.
But I won't float away, sir,
If you're not around.

Goodbye, au revoir!
Sayonara, vamoose!
You've been a good shadow.
Now scram, my caboose!

The Missing Nose

I'm missing a nose. Have you seen it around?
It's not that red thing, that one's from a clown.
I looked under the bed and inside of a book
I can't smell anything, can you help me look?
I might have left it at Aunt Nelly's place.
Can you give her a call and ask her, in case?
Or maybe I left it when we went to the store.
Or in the back of a taxi. Or at the lakeshore.
I'm afraid it's gone without a trace.
I should have just kept it where it was on my face.

I Once Found A Stick

I once found a stick
And was waving it around.
And it spoke to me
And that's how I found
It didn't like being waved.
It didn't like being flicked.
I was making it dizzy.
I was making it sick.
"Can you please stop," it said,
"This spinning around?
I am feeling quite squeamish.
Can you please put me down?"
But I didn't, and then
It just barfed in my face.
Broken leaves and sticky sap
All over the place.
So I asked myself, "Why,
Of all the sticks in the world,
Did I have to find one
That got sick from being twirled?"

Someone Has Taken My Pants

I checked the laundry, and the kitchen,
And the shower and the stair.
I checked the pantry and the closet.
My pants are just not there.

I checked the washroom and the playroom,
And the attic and the deck.
My pants are gone, I must report
There's nowhere left to check.

I looked inside,
I looked outside,
I looked upstairs,

I looked down.
I cannot find
My pants at all.
They simply
Can't be found.

I think they ran away last night.
They're not where they belong:
In the top drawer on the right,
Beside the–

Oh, what do you know.
They were here all along.

The Other Me

I was walking along
And ran into me.
It was quite a surprise
I'm sure you'd agree.
It was another me
Going the opposite way.
I'd never seen anything
Like that in my day.

The other me was running
From what I don't know.
He seemed in a panic
And needed to go.
He fled down the stairs
And straight out the door.
And after that, I couldn't see
Him anymore.

He didn't say sorry
He didn't say why
But I could see fear and
Surprise in his eyes.

That was a strange thing
What should I do?
No one would believe me
Not even you.

I needed to proceed.
I needed to go.
So I went on my way
From a moment ago.

But after two steps
I sensed something wrong.
I heard a loud hiss.
And it stank, really strong.
It was coming from a door
Two steps to my right.
And I stopped in my tracks
As anyone might.

And the door cracked open.
I could see through the gap,
There was a thing with red eyes
And it seemed really mad!
And that thing by the door,
It started to roar.
So I had to flee
Right away, I was sure.

So, I turned and I ran
In the opposite way
And bumped into that me again
I'm sorry to say.
He was walking upstairs
And seemed unaware
Of the very bad thing
That was waiting up there.

He was standing where I was
A moment ago.
And looked quite surprised,
And shocked me, don't you know.

But I couldn't say sorry,
I couldn't say why,
I needed to flee
From that thing with red eyes.

So I pushed right past him
And ran out the door
And I don't know what came of
That me anymore.
I hope I run into
That me someday.
So I can find out
How he got away.

Duck in a Dog's Body

There once was a dog who thought he was a duck.
He quacked a lot and sometimes clucked
One day he laid eggs in the barn by the hay.
Everyone who was there was amazed that day.

"That doesn't seem right," said the chicken, who knew.
"Dogs don't lay eggs. That's just not true!"
The dog just shrugged. "I don't know what you heard.
But I'm not a dog. I'm just a bird."

"How can that be?" asked the chicken in shock.
"It's a common thing," said the dog with a squawk.

So he sat on those eggs for many a day.
He sat on them long, and every which way.
And they started to hatch, and out came some chicks.
But they barked instead of quacking and chewed on sticks.

"I can't believe this," the chicken clucked in awe.
"They act like dogs, even licking their paws!"
"You think that's strange?" responded the dog.
"I just found out their dad's a frog!"

Who Wants an Ice Cream Sandwich?

Do you think you could try my ice cream sandwich?
It has the best flavors, even some outlandish.
Vanilla and chocolate and strawberry to start,
Sprinkles and marshmallows and small candy hearts.
And graham cracker crumbles and a slice of cheese
And ketchup, tomatoes, and pickles, to please
And an olive on top, to add some appeal
And spaghetti and meatballs – your favorite meal!
And ham and potatoes and spinach and kale
And pancakes and syrup, how can that fail?
And to top it all off, some hot cherry pie.
And some raspberry syrup, don't ask me why.
If that sounds delicious, I'll make you one quick.
Now, why are you saying, you're gonna be sick?

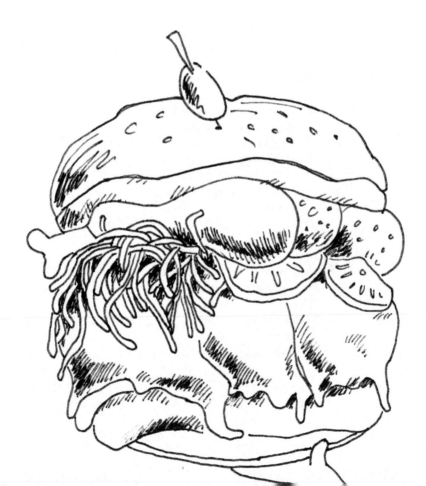

Cynthia Blue Would
Not Wear Shoes

She walked in bare feet
All over the street
On meadows and roads
With ten tiny toes
On sidewalks and lanes
Up hills and the plains
On bridges and roads
In the rain and the snow

"Even in snow? you ask.
"Yes, even in snow."
"Wasn't that cold?" you say.
"Yes, certainly so."

So, her feet got all worn.
Treads tattered and torn,
Her skin split and cracked.
Like an elephant's back.
And she didn't keep them clean
So they turned a dark green.
And a leathery skin grew,
Resembling a shoe.
With a sole thick and hard.
Like a box or a card.
Like the skin of a book.
Or a horse's hoof.
Until she walked on a pebble,
And didn't even quibble.

But one day in May
Those feet gave away.
She'd been walking in snow
Everywhere she could go
And they just wore out
Like a tired old trout.

She told them to walk
But they sat like a rock.
They'd no longer go,
Even if she said so.

So, she went to the store
With her mom, Eleanor.
And they bought her some feet.
They were new, they were neat.
And they fit her so well,
Like a clam to a shell,
Like a hat to a hook
Or page to a book.
And her mom checked the price,
And that would suffice.

But there was one snag,
Her mom waved at the bag:
"If we buy these new feet,
You must keep them neat.
You can't leave them in snow,
Or fill them with dough,
Or paint them pink,
Or dip them in ink,
Or loan them to monkeys,
Or anything junky."

"Okay," Cindy agreed,
More in words than in deed.
But she bid an adieu
To the old Cindy Blue.
And with her new feet
She hit the street.
In the snow and the hail
Without any fail.
In the rain and the sleet.
But not with bare feet.
She wore shoes every day.
In every which way.
And did this for years
Or so it appears.
Until age thirty-two
When her feet were still new,
Because Cynthia Blue
Always wore shoes.

Grown Ups Are Crazy People

Grownups are crazy people, I have to say
Why must everything be put away?
And why must we clean, 'cause you know, it's just hard?
I have dirty feet – but I was just in the yard!

Sometimes we'll be late, it's okay, not a crime.
I think you're obsessed with this thing called time.
Promptness and lateness, that stuff's in your head.
Sometimes I need to stay longer in bed.

If there's a booger, I'll pick my nose.
I'm sorry you don't like it, but that's how it goes.
If I split my pants, it's okay, not the end.
I can always get an extra pair from one of my friends.

Giant Footprint

We found a giant footprint out in the yard.
Something big stepped there and smushed the ground hard.
We think it's a giant or a big kangaroo,
Or maybe a kid with some oversized shoes,
Or perhaps it's an angel or a golem or a troll,
Or maybe some person out digging a hole.
Whatever it is left a print ten yards wide.
If it comes back later, I think we should hide.

Art on the Wall

I was trying to hang a picture,
But instead, I hung my nose.
I was dangling from the wall alone.
It wasn't a pretty pose.

When momma found me, her eyes lit up.
She loved the art on the wall.
She called all her friends and showed me to them.
And they raved in delight, one and all.

"It looks like a monster," one woman said.
"No, it's a dog," said a man, "on a cart."
"It looks like a camel," said another.
"Where'd you find it?"
"My son," said my ma. "He's got art."

And they said I was brilliant. They said I was original.
It was genius, the things that I did.
But when they went home, ma set me down.
Not Mona Lisa, just a kid.

Worst Day

Who put a corncob in my bed?
Who put a gumdrop on my head?
Who put a diaper in the car?
Who put a doll's head in a jar?
Who put a golf ball in my hat?
Who put a shark mask on the cat?
Who put an onion in my drink?
Who put my sneakers in the sink?
Who put my briefcase on the deck?
Who drew a circle on my neck?

Who put my suitcase in the pool?
Who put an orange in my tools?
Who put meatballs in my chair?
Who put a crayon in my hair?
Who taped a pencil to my pen?
Who did it twice, and then again?

Okay, I've had enough!
This is the worst!
What's that you say?
It's April first?

I Taught A Horse to Talk

I taught a horse to talk
You'd be surprised what he said.
"Why do you ride on my back?
I don't sleep on your head.
Why do keep me in a barn?
I don't lock you in bed.
I don't like this saddle.
I want a soft one instead."
Then he took a big bite
From my straw hat,
Chewed it and said,
"I'd like mustard with that."

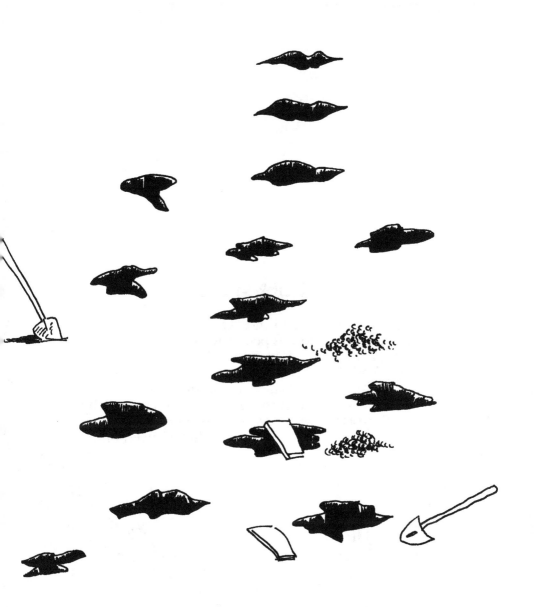

Buried Treasure

We heard there's buried treasure
Somewhere in the yard.
A few more holes, we'll find some gold.
It can't be all that hard.

We dug so many holes today,
My arm is really sore.
No gems or coins, but there's one plus:
No mowing the lawn anymore.

Bubble Gum

My momma told me, "One gum, not two."
But I thought, more is better, what harm could it do?
So I chewed two gums and blew a big bubble.
And then I found I was in some trouble.
The bubble floated up, up up in the sky.
We're drifting with the clouds, don't ask me why.
I'm worried we're getting too close to the sun.
Can you get me a ladder? I think I need one.

Lost Sock

The other day we found a sock.
It was in the yard by the pile of rocks.
How do you lose a sock and not even know?
When you walk, you'll feel the ground on your toes.
My mom picked it up and said, "Is this yours?"
I thought that was silly, cause we were outdoors.
But I checked my feet, and my socks were gone!
Two bare feet, right on the lawn!
So I put it on, my foot's not bare.
If I find the other, I'll have a pair.

Mikey Might Have Been

Mikey might have been a gymnast,
  but the bars were too high.
Mikey might have been a painter,
  but he didn't have the eye.

Mikey might have been a lifeguard,
  but the sand was too hot.
Mikey might have been a golfer,
  but he never took a shot.

Mikey might have been a spaceman,
  but the suit made him sweaty.
Mikey might have been a chef,
  but he couldn't make spaghetti.

Mikey might have been a climber,
but he didn't like the heights.
Mikey might have been a dancer,
but the outfit was too tight.

Mikey might have been a pianist,
but he couldn't reach the keys.
Mikey might have been a baker,
but the flour made him sneeze.

Mikey might have been a fiddler,
but the strings were too long.
Mikey might have been a singer,
but he couldn't learn a song

Mikey might have been a doctor,
but he didn't like disease.
Mikey might have been a logger,
but he couldn't hurt the trees.

Mikey might have been a goalie,
but he couldn't stop the ball.
Mikey might have been a pilot, but
the cockpit was too small.

Mikey might have been successful,
but he didn't really try.
No one told him to be better.
Maybe that's the reason why?

The Bestest Animal
in the World

The rabbit was bragging to all who could hear,
"Just look," he boasted. "What fabulous ears!
They can hear far away, over mountains, quite far,
They're the bestest of all, the bestest there are."

"So modest," hissed the skunk. "But I think you're mistaken.
I've got a stink so strong that the dead can awaken.
And two beautiful colors, some black and some white,
I'm the most fearsome thing you can encounter at night."

"You stink," growled the frog. "But can you croak like a toad?
Our cries carry far, even over the road.
I'm part fish and part reptile, the best in between.
With a skin that is slimy and all shades of green."

"You might babble," snapped the dog. "But I'm faster than you.
There is very little actually that a dog can't do.
We catch balls, we swim, and smell things really far,
And we howl at the moon, we're the best that there are."

"Howling?" chirped the squirrel. "You think that's the best?
I stash berries and nuts and build a fine nest.
You others don't plan. You don't prepare like me.
There's nothing any better than a squirrel, you see."

"Nuts," cawed the crow. "That's crazy, that's absurd!
To think that a squirrel is the best in the world.
Crows are the best, we are black and have wings,
And our voices are strong when each of us sings."

"Singing?" huffed the kangaroo. "I think that's a miss."
He tapped his pouch. "What animal has this?
A pocket! A pocket! Who doesn't need such a thing!
You can keep stuff in it, and don't lose what you bring!"

"You're mistaken my friends," groaned the great blue whale.
"You've forgotten the fish with an air hole and tail.
There's no finer, faster fish in the ocean, you'll see.
Who breathes and eats plankton, no other like me."

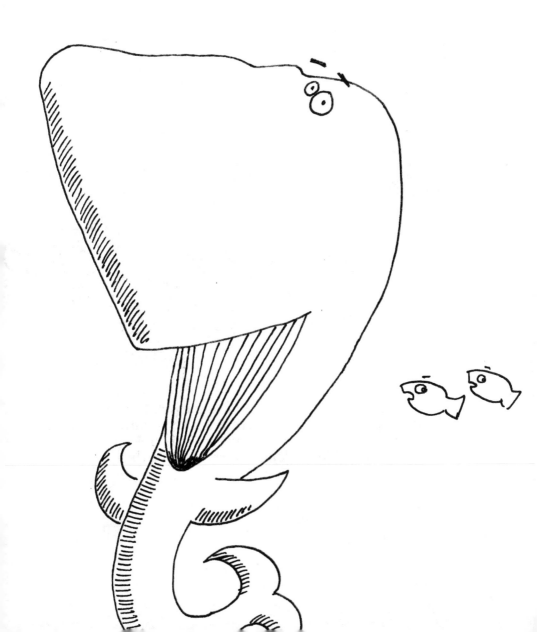

"A tail?" howled the lemur. "I have a much finer tail.
It has rings and I can hang from it all day with no fail.
It can hold a banana as I fly through the trees.
Every monkey I know longs to have one of these."

"Your tail," croaked the toucan, "Has nothing on my beak.
I'm a beauty of the jungle, with a glorious physique.
I have wings and feathers and great colors to please.
I can't think of any other who has talents like these."

"Talents?" clicked the dolphin. "I have talents galore.
I can see underwater with my ears, only more.
I can leap in the air, do flips, I can speak.
I don't think any of you are as truly unique."

"Madness," gasped the oyster. "You're all clowns in my book.
I clean the ocean of gunk and build shells, take a look.
I don't make noise or make waves, but I do plenty you see.
There's hardly any animal as useful as me."

"Useful is not best," yipped the fox. "I'm smart and I'm sly.
I have a stunning winter coat that's attractive to the eye.
You all can't compare, I am the best of them all.
There is nothing in the forest like a fox, big or small."

"Do you have this?" the lobster waved his bulging claw.
"I can cut through a tin can like a mechanic's saw.
We're prized by the people and taste delicious I hear.
You others can't compare, you don't even come near."

"You taste good?" clucked the pickle. "That's your claim to be best?
If that's the case, then perhaps I'm the best of the rest.
I taste sour but I'm crisp, and I keep really long,
If you stay long enough, I'll sing you my song."

"What animal is this?" they pondered, and could he be best?
They decided to check and put him to the test.
The rabbit took a nibble, and the others took a bite.
When the last of him was gone, they agreed, he was right.

Sandy Sedd

I once knew a girl named
Sandy Sedd,
Whose reflection said to
move her head.
She looked away, and her
double did too,
Then it grimaced once
and waved her to shoo.

"You're blocking my view,"
the reflection said.
"I can't see anything beyond
your head.
There's a world out there,
and stuff to do.
But I can't see anything
except for you."

Sandy was shocked, how could this be?
Her mirror was suddenly
being so mean.
This was not good behavior,
she knew to be true.
These were actions her teachers at school
would call rude.

"You need to say sorry," she waved in the air.
"Your job is to smile when I'm combing my hair.

I'm not moving once
   until you agree.
      We can stay here forever,
      just wait and you'll see."

      So they stayed that way
      for a year and a day,
      Waiting for one to move,
      or the other to obey.
      Until her reflection sighed
      and said, "Oy vey!"
      And quit and now has been
      gone to this day.

      Then for Sandy, things got kind
      of weird.
      In the mirror, for her, no reflection
   appeared.
It was hard to explain, it was hard to
believe
That nothing appeared in the mirror to
see.

   But I spoke to her reflection, and it
      whispered to me,
   It would come back, one day, it finally agreed.
   And was willing to overlook previous deeds.
... if Sandy would just say, "Please."

The Duck Who
Played Chess

There once was a duck who liked to play chess.
He thought he was perfect, he thought he was the best.
The truth is he cheated, and that's how he won.
He was playing the dog, who did not find that fun.

"You're moving the pieces," the dog looked confused.
"Not true," quacked the duck, "But you're going to lose."
Then the dog turned away, attracted by a fly.
And the duck stole his queen, in the blink of an eye.

"You're easily distracted," said the duck, with a wink.
"Not true," huffed the dog. "I just need to think."
"When you turn your head, your whole body goes round."
"That's how I think," the dog circled twice then sat down.

"Where's my queen?" the dog stopped and finally noticed.
"It's gone," clucked the duck, "You must really focus."
The dog checked the board and scrunched up his eyes.
"I think the game's over," he said with a sigh.

Then the dog turned the board a hundred-eighty degrees
So their pieces were switched. "Your turn," he said, pleased.
"What happened?" squawked the duck, "Did you do something?"
"You lost," said the dog, as he swallowed the king.

Dancing in the Snow

My momma warned me about liking the snow.
"It don't stick around," she said, "That's just how it goes."
But I wanted to play with a new winter friend
"I don't think," she said, "You're gonna like how it ends."

But I couldn't shake the thought of that friend from my head
Despite all the things that my momma said.
So I snuck out my window to see if it's true
That a snowman really knows what a girl likes to do!

He was waiting for me in some snappy clothes
And a black top hat and carrot nose.
When he saw me he smiled, and I knew instantly
This would be quite a magical night out for me.

"Let's go dancing," he said, and he took my hand
And we danced until late at a place with a band.
He danced so well I knew I was right
To stay out late and accept his invite.

But when midnight struck, he had to leave.
"Got to hide from the sun until tomorrow eve."
He gave me a hug, and he said good night.
A snowman really knows how to treat a girl right!

And I went to bed, but I couldn't rest.
I kept thinking about him. My friend was the best!.
But my momma did not really seem to agree.
She warned, "It's not gonna work out, you'll see."

The next night, we went sledding and made angels in the snow.
It was a dream date, I thought, as far as that goes.
But when midnight came, he left in a rush.
He couldn't stay, he said, or he'd turn to slush.

He was stuck in my head, the whole next day.
I thought of things to do and what to say.
I thought of great parties that we could attend
And is he just snow or my new best friend?

The next night, we went out to a place by the lake
Where the snowmen were having an oyster bake.
And we danced all night and mopped up the floor.
But when he had to leave, I said, "One more?"

So we danced and danced and forgot the time
And the sun came up, it was quarter to nine!
"Oh dear," he said. "I forgot to go.
It's gonna get hot, and that's not good for snow!"

And he started to sweat, and he started to thaw.
I wasn't sure he could make it at all.
But before he was gone, he had this to say.
Which I'll remember always, to the end of my days:

"Treat every day," he said,
"Like a gem of ice.
Squeeze it real hard.
It won't be here twice.
And what it all meant,
One day you will know
But in the meantime,
Have a dance in the snow."

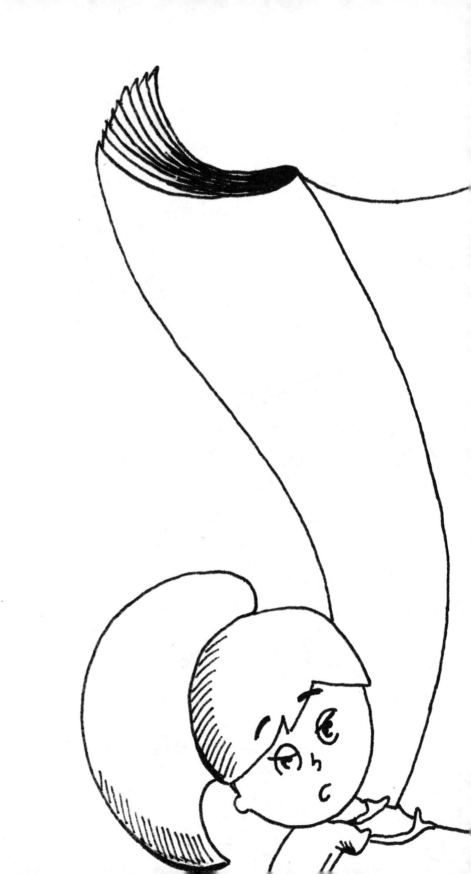

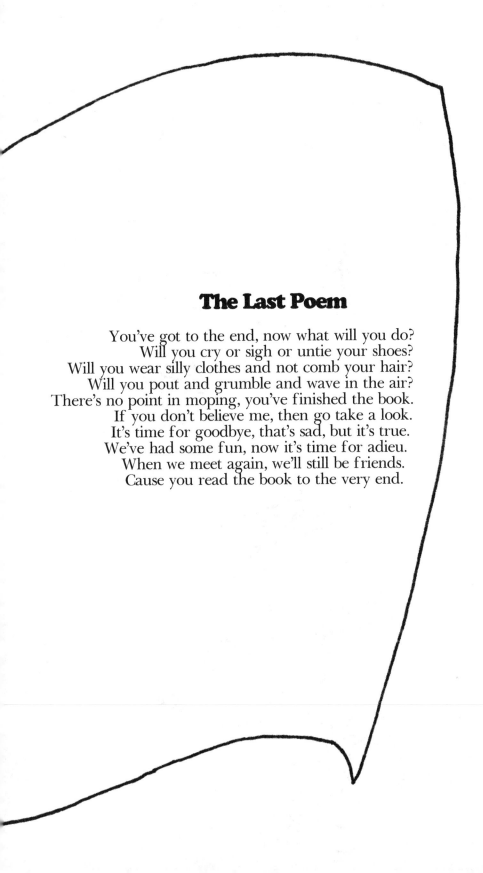

The Last Poem

You've got to the end, now what will you do?
Will you cry or sigh or untie your shoes?
Will you wear silly clothes and not comb your hair?
Will you pout and grumble and wave in the air?
There's no point in moping, you've finished the book.
If you don't believe me, then go take a look.
It's time for goodbye, that's sad, but it's true.
We've had some fun, now it's time for adieu.
When we meet again, we'll still be friends.
Cause you read the book to the very end.

Acknowledgements

Every book requires the efforts of many individuals, and this one is no exception. I want to give a heartfelt thanks to the following individuals, who helped make it happen: Amadeus, Samantha at Raven's Wing Editing, Danielle Lynn, Emily Dickinson, Stacey Shaneyfelt, Matt Cubberly, Sandra Falkenstein, Carey Dean, Zaina Zia Syed, Class of 2021 at Miss Zainab's Academy, Efa Eval Ele, Josh Soule, and Sherri Habben. Paul Hawkins, design ninja, raised the book to a whole new level. Also, special thanks to my wife Weiqun and my daughter Catalina for bearing with me and helping me decide the things I couldn't decide myself.

INDEX

Looking for More?

Thanks for reading *What's Wrong with a Pet Dinosaur?* I hope you enjoyed it. If you want to read more, sign up for my email list and I'll send you free a bonus book, *The Last Flower in the Flowerpot*. It's only available on TonyPhilips.com.

I'll also send you infrequent info on forthcoming books, events, appearances and more.

Feedback Wanted!

If you liked this book, please post a review on your favorite online bookstore. Even a short review makes a big difference. Reviews are invaluable for authors like me and books like this one!

About the Author

Tony Philips grew up in a suburb in Pennsylvania near a turkey farm. Every so often, frantic turkeys, escaped from the farm, would show up in his back yard, and he and his siblings would try to hide them. Have you ever tried to usher a crazed turkey behind a bush? It's not easy. He attended art classes at the Baum School of Art and got a degree in Creative Writing from Haverford College. He tried writing for television, but nobody wanted to hear his stories about freaked out turkeys. Or about how an unhinged turkey one time bit his younger brother on the toe. It's true, really. Tony lives in Chicago with his wife and daughter. This is his first children's book.

Printed in the USA
CPSIA information can be obtained
at www.ICGtesting.com
LVHW011955280823
756442LV00096B/306/J